C000060197

# PUNCTUATION

## RULES and PRACTICE 2

Susan J. Daughtrey M.Ed.

Childs World Education Limited
Revised 2005

# CONTENTS

# SPEECH

## DIRECT AND REPORTED SPEECH

**Speech marks are used to enclose actual words spoken. This is called DIRECT SPEECH.**

**Speech marks (" "), often called *inverted commas*, can be pairs of single or double raised commas. Either is correct as long as you are consistent.**
Example:

> "I am going home," said Michael.
> 'I am going home,' said Michael.

**REPORTED, sometimes called INDIRECT SPEECH, is not spoken. Rather, it is a *report* of what was spoken. It tells what the speaker said without necessarily using his exact words. *Reported speech* does not contain speech marks.**
Example:

> Michael said that he was going home.

Here there are no speech marks. Michael is not speaking. We are not writing down the words actually spoken. Rather, it is a *report* of what Michael said.

## PRACTICE : DIRECT and REPORTED SPEECH

> **Actual words spoken by someone is called DIRECT SPEECH.**
> **Speech marks, or *inverted commas*, are used to enclose the actual words spoken.**
> **REPORTED or INDIRECT SPEECH is not spoken.**
> **It is a *report* of what was spoken.**
> ***Reported speech* does not contain speech marks.**

**Exercise One:** _____

Write *D* for *direct speech* or *R* for *reported speech* at the end of each of these sentences. Speech marks have been deliberately left out of the *direct speech*.

Example:

| | |
|---|---|
| Please close that door, said the lady. | (_D_) |
| She said that she never wanted to see him again. | (_R_) |

1. The old lady asked Mary to close the door.                  (___)

2. You can go now said the teacher to her class.                (___)

3. We are going abroad for our holiday this year, said Bernard.   (___)

4.   Bernard said that he was going abroad for his holiday this year.     (___)

5.   She said she would do her homework later.                           (___)

6.   Hold tight! shouted the bus conductor.                             (___)

7.   She said she never wanted to see him again.                        (___)

8.   Why are you late? asked the referee.                              (___)

9.   The doctor said, Take the medicine twice a day.                   (___)

10.  The athlete wondered why everyone was cheering.                   (___)

# REPORTED SPEECH

**1. The use of a connecting word** which links the reporting word (such as *said*) to the speech. Often the word *that* is used.
Example:

> She said, "I am feeling hungry."          (Direct Speech)
> She said (*that*) she was feeling hungry.     (Reported Speech)

It is often omitted, however, when the word following the *connecting word* is the person. In these cases, to put in the connecting word or not, either is acceptable.

**2. The tense of the verb may change when speech is reported.**
Example:

> Michael says, "I am going home."        (Direct speech, present tense)

**If this is *reported* using a *past* reporting verb (*said*) the tense of the verb in the words spoken changes.**
Example:

> Michael *said* that he *was* going home.

Here, the verb *says* is changed to *said* (*past* reporting verb); the verb in the words spoken I *am* (*present* tense) changes to he *was (past tense)*.

**If, on the other hand, speech is reported using a *present* reporting verb (*says*), the tense of the words spoken does not change.**
Example:

> Michael says, "I am going home."          (Direct speech)
> Michael *says* that he *is* going home.      (Reported speech)

Here the verb *says* is kept (*present* reporting verb). The tense of the verb in the words spoken is not changed.

Example:

| | |
|---|---|
| "I am hungry," says Christine. | (Direct speech, present tense) |
| Christine *said* (that) she *was* hungry. | (*Past* reporting verb) |
| Christine *says* (that) she *is* hungry. | (*Present* reporting verb) |

When a *past* reporting verb is used, it is as if the action *moves back* in time and the verb which is in the present tense in the words *spoken*, moves back and becomes words *reported* in the past tense.

Similarly, if the tense of the verb in the words spoken is already in the past, this normally, but not always, *moves back* in time still further. If it does not move back further it stays in the same past tense as it is in the direct speech.

Example:

"I spoke to him yesterday, but he took no notice," said the secretary.
(Direct speech, past tense)

The secretary said that she *had spoken* to him yesterday but he *had taken* no notice. Here the tense of the spoken verb *moves back* in time further.

OR    The secretary said that she *spoke* to him yesterday but he *took* no notice. Here, the tense of the *spoken* verb does not change. It stays in the same tense as the verb in the direct speech.

Either tense of the verb in the *spoken* word is acceptable.

**When a *past* reporting verb (*said*) is used, a verb already in the past tense in the spoken word either moves back further in time, or stays in the same past tense as it is in the direct speech.**

Similarly, verbs already in the *past perfect* (the action has been completed) may not change at all.
Example:

"I *had* chicken and chips for lunch," said the little girl.
The little girl said (that) she *had* chicken and chips for lunch.
OR:       The little girl said (that) she *had had* chicken and chips for lunch.

In these cases, the verb may move back further in time or remain in the same tense as the spoken verb in the direct speech.

**The tense of the spoken verb may not change if what is true when the words are spoken in direct speech remains true when the words are reported.**
Example:

"There are fifty-four million people in Britain," he said.
He said that there *are* fifty-four million people in Britain.
He said that there *were* fifty-four million people in Britain.

It is up to the reporter. To use the present or past tense in the reported speech would be equally acceptable.

"I live in Skegness," said the lady.

The lady said that she *lives* in Skegness.

The lady said that she *lived* in Skegness.

Either is acceptable though strictly speaking to keep the verb in the same tense as the spoken verb in the direct speech must be technically more accurate.

Note these verbs which change in the past tense:

*go* becomes *went*; *can* becomes *could*; *will* becomes *would*; *may* becomes *might*.

The past tense of the verbs *could*, *would*, *should* and *might* do not change in reported speech.

Example:

"I might be able to come," said the boy.

The boy said (that) he *might* be able to come.

"I would like a sweet," said Tom.

Tom said (that) he *would* like a sweet.

**When there is a difference between what is true and what is said, the tense of the verb changes.**

Example:

"I *am* eighteen," said the youth.

The youth said that he *was* eighteen, but in fact he *is* only seventeen.

**3. The (*personal*) pronoun *I* is changed to *he, she,* or *it*.**

The person speaking *I* (*first person singular*) is now being spoken *about* so the third person singular, *he, she* or *it* is required. In the same way the first person plural (*we*) is changed to the third person plural, *they*.

Example:

"*I* love chocolate," said the fat lady.

The fat lady said that *she* loved chocolate.

The boy asked, "When can *I* use the computer?"

The boy asked when could *he* use the computer.

**The (*possessive*) pronouns *my* and *our* also change in reported speech to *his* and *their*.**

Example:

Direct speech:          "Will *you* be *my* friend?" he asked Mavis.

Indirect speech:      He asked Mavis if *she* would be *his* friend.

"*Our* dog is the best!" retorted the twins.

The twins retorted *their* dog was the best.

Or                        The twins retorted their dog *is* the best,

if this remains true at the time of reporting!

**4. People talking about the place where they are and the time about which they are speaking often changes in reported speech.**

Example:

*here* becomes *there*

*now* becomes *then*

*this* becomes *that*

*these* becomes *those*

Reference to *today, tonight, yesterday* or *tomorrow* by the speaker has to be reworded to *that day, that night, the previous day* or *day before, the following* or *next day.*

*next Sunday* becomes the *following Sunday*

*last Thursday* becomes the *previous Thursday*

Example:

"I am *here* on holiday until *next Sunday,*" said Sara.

Sara said (that) she was *there* on holiday until *the following Sunday.*

Common sense must determine when and in what way, time and place is altered in reported speech.

Example:

"I will meet you *here tomorrow,*" said Sally.

If these words are being reported the next day it might be:

Sally said (that) she would meet me *there* (or *here*) *today.*

## 5. If there is a question word in the direct speech it can remain in the reported speech.

Example:

"*Who* will be my girl friend?" he asked.

He asked *who* would be his girl friend.

"*Where* is the headmaster's study?" the visitor enquired.

The visitor enquired *where* was the headmaster's study.

## However, if there was no question word, introduce the words spoken with *if* or *whether.*

Example:

"Will you come inside?" asked the lady.

The lady asked *if* she would go inside.

If there is no question word, such as *what, when, which, why* or *how,* as in the final example, follow the reporting verb (*asked*) with the connecting word *if* or *whether.*

## In *reported* questions the auxiliary verb *do, does* or *did* is not used.

Example:

"What do you want James?" I asked.

I asked James what he wanted.

"Where do you live, Gina?" asked Barry.

Barry asked Gina where she lived.

## 6. Change any command into the infinitive of the verb (*to* do something).

Example:

"*Close* the door!" he shouted to them.

He shouted to them *to close* the door.

"*Come* and *join* me here, tomorrow," Harry told the boys.
Harry told the boys *to go* and (*to*) *join* him there the following day.

**7. When the command (or promise) is in the negative, use *not* with the infinitive of the verb.**

Example:

"*Don't paint* that!" yelled the lady.
The lady yelled *not to paint* that.
"I *won't be* late," promised the boy.
The boy promised *not to be* late.

# PRACTICE : REPORTED SPEECH

**In REPORTED SPEECH:**

**1. A connecting word such as *that* is usually used except when the word following is the person, in which case *that* can be omitted.**

**2. The tense of the verb may change.**
**When the words are spoken *in the present*,**
**the tense of the *spoken verb*:**
    **a. *moves back in time* when a *past* reporting verb is used.**
    **b. *remains the same* when a *present* reporting verb is used.**
**When the words were spoken *in the past*,**
**the tense of the *spoken verb*:**
    **c. either *moves back* still further, or *remains the same*.**
**The tense may not change if what is true when the words are spoken in direct speech remains true when the words are reported. When there is a difference between what is true and what is said, the tense of the verb changes.**

**3. Personal and possessive pronouns:**
**pronouns in the first person are changed to**
**pronouns in the third person (singular or plural).**

**4. Places and times often change.**

**5. Question words in direct speech remain in reported speech.**
**Where there is no question word use *if* or *whether*.**
**The auxiliary verb *do, does, did* is not used in reported questions.**

**6. Change a command into the infinitive of the verb.**

**7. Where a command or promise is in the negative, use *not* with the infinitive.**

## Exercise Two:_____

The sentences below are in *DIRECT SPEECH*. Read through the Rule Summary above and then
rewrite each sentence in *REPORTED SPEECH* making as many changes as are necessary.
Use the same tense in the *reporting* verb as the *italicised* verb in each question. Remember if you are
using a past *reporting* verb, the present tense of a verb in the words spoken moves back in time.
Example:

> "I **am** giving up tennis," *said* the men's champion. (*said* past tense)
> The men's champion *said* that he **was** giving up tennis. (spoken verb changes)

Underneath note the changes you have made with reference to the Rule Summaries above. Like this:

> The connecting word *that* can be used. (Point 1)
> The past tense (*said)* of the reporting verb is used so the tense of the verb used in the words
actually spoken changes and moves back in time (**was**). (Point 2a)
> The personal pronoun *I* changes to *he.* (Point 3)

1.  "Where are we going today?" *asked* Barry.

2.  "Where is the cinema?" David *asks*.

3.  "The number is engaged," *said* the operator.

4.  "I may be able to go swimming," *said* the boy.

5.  "Close the door, Sam!" *shouted* Maria.

6.  "What do you want, Barnaby?" *asked* the teacher.

7.  "I'll not do that again," *promised* Jack.

8.  "Come on time, Robert," *said* Louise.

9.  "We will meet here again next Sunday," *said* Rev. Simms.

10. "My brother is eighteen," *said* Timothy.


## Exercise Three: _____

Do as you did in Exercise Two above. Rewrite the following sentences changing the *DIRECT SPEECH*
into *REPORTED SPEECH*. Make as many changes as are necessary. Use the same tense in the
*reporting* verb as the *italicised* verb in each question. Underneath note the changes you have made with
reference to the Rule Summaries above.

1.  "Tomorrow, we shall go to the cinema," mother *said*.

2.  "Shut up and sit down!" *yelled* the teacher.

3.  "Where do you live, Sandra?" *asked* Helen.

4.  "I may go," *said* Christopher.

5.  "I live in Spain," *said* the bronzed youth.

6.  "I swam six lengths of the pool today," *said* Arthur.

7.  "There are twenty-eight pupils in my class," *said* Cheri.

8.  "Close that window!" *shouted* the gardener.

9.  "I won't be long," *promised* Michael.

10  "Will you have a cup of tea?" *asks* the old lady.

# DIRECT SPEECH

**Whenever you are writing *the actual words spoken by someone*, you are writing DIRECT SPEECH. In direct speech a pair of speech marks (" ") or (' ') must be used.**

When writing direct speech there are several important points that must be remembered:

1. **Speech marks are always used in pairs.** The whole of the sentence spoken, including the punctuation mark at the end of the sentence, is enclosed between two pairs of speech marks. These may be pairs of single or double raised commas.

2. **Only the words spoken come between the speech marks.** Words added by the story-teller are placed outside the speech marks and separated from it, usually by a comma.
Example:
> "I am going to play hockey on Saturday," said Louise.

Here, the words actually spoken by Louise are enclosed in speech marks. It is not necessary to enclose *said Louise* as these words were not spoken. They must, therefore, remain outside the speech marks and be separated from the words inside the speech marks by a comma.

3. **In DIRECT SPEECH, the punctuation of the sentence being spoken remains unchanged and goes inside the speech marks.**
The sentence begins with a capital letter and may end with a full stop, question mark or exclamation mark.
Example:
> Are you going to Spain tomorrow?

If these words were spoken by someone, we would write:
> "Are you going to Spain tomorrow?" she asked.

Here the punctuation of the words actually spoken remains unchanged. The speech marks completely enclose the sentence spoken together with its punctuation.
(If the sentence had ended in a full stop, the final full stop would have been changed to a comma before the words *she said* were added.)

**4. The first word actually spoken ALWAYS begins with a capital letter.**

# THE THREE PATTERNS OF DIRECT SPEECH

It is possible to identify **three** patterns of writing direct speech.

---

"CL_____," he said.

He said, "CL_____."

"CL_____," he said, "sl_____."

---

Key: CL = capital letter    sl = small letter

Let us look at these three patterns in detail.

**Pattern One:**
*he said* comes at the end of the sentence. We can represent this:

"CL_____," he said.

CL = capital letter

1. Make the first letter of the first word spoken a capital letter.
2. Change the full stop at the end of the words spoken into a comma.
   (However, a question or exclamation mark would not change.)
3. Enclose the words spoken in speech marks.
4. Continue with *he said*, small *h*. (Regardless of which final punctuation mark
   is used at the end of the words spoken - point 2 above.)
5. Put a full stop at the end of the sentence.

Example:
"I like roller skating," he said.
1                              2 4        5

**Pattern Two:**
*he said* (*he asked*) comes at the beginning of the sentence. We can represent this:

He said, "CL_____."

CL = Capital letter

1. Put a comma after *said* and before the opening speech mark.
2. Open the speech marks and begin the word actually spoken with a capital letter.
3. The punctuation that belongs to the actual words spoken remains unchanged inside the final speech mark.

Example:

He asked, "Can I have my pocket-money now?"
1 2                                          3

**Pattern Three:**

*he said* comes in the middle of the words actually spoken, thereby breaking what is said into two parts. The pattern is like this:

"CL_____," he said, "sl_____."

CL = Capital letter   sl = small letter

Example:

"I think," said Jenny, "we'll go for a walk after lunch."
1      4              4 5                              3

Here the sentence being spoken is:

"I think we'll go for a walk after lunch."

1. It is regularly punctuated with a capital letter at the beginning of the sentence and a full stop at the end.
2. Speech marks enclose the words actually spoken.
3. All the punctuation belonging to the sentence remains unchanged and inside the speech marks.

*said Jenny* is placed into the middle of the words being spoken. It is necessary, therefore, to use two pairs of speech marks, but no need to have two capital letters as it is only one sentence that is being spoken even though it is in two parts.

4. A comma is inserted at the end of the first part spoken and another after *said Jenny* (before the opening pair of the second set of speech marks).
5. The first letter of the first word in the second set of speech marks is a small letter as it is a continuation of the one sentence being spoken.

In all three patterns, the following points can be noted:
1. ALWAYS begin the first word spoken with a capital letter.
2. There is ALWAYS a comma immediately in front of the opening pair of speech marks.
3. ALWAYS put a punctuation mark at the end of the words spoken. This can be a full stop, exclamation mark or question mark. However, if the sentence continues with *he said* (or similar expression), a full stop (only) is changed to a comma.
4. All the punctuation that belongs to the words spoken remains unchanged and goes INSIDE the speech marks.
5. In patterns One and Three, *he* always begins with a small letter even though this may follow a question or exclamation mark that belongs to the words spoken.

Let us look at all these points in these sentences:

"Have you read your library book?" asked Robert.

(Pattern One)

James said, "I love burger and chips."

(Pattern Two)

"If you'll be my friend," said Alice, "you can come to my party."

(Pattern Three)

In all these sentences:
1. The first word of the sentence spoken begins with a capital letter.
2. There is ALWAYS a comma immediately in front of the opening pair of speech marks (Patterns 2 and 3).
3. There is a punctuation mark at the end of the words spoken. This punctuation mark remains unchanged and in these cases, is the mark that would be there if the words were not spoken. This would always be the case except in Pattern One where a full stop (only) would change to a comma before continuing with *he said*.
4. All the punctuation of the words spoken goes inside the speech marks.
5. In Patterns 1 and 3 the first word following the final speech mark begins with a small letter even though in the case of the sentence in Pattern 1 above, the words spoken end in a question mark. Only in Pattern 2 does *he (James)* begin with a capital letter at the beginning of the sentence.

A special case:
If the question or exclamation mark belongs to the words spoken, it goes *inside* the speech marks. If however, the question or exclamation mark is not part of the spoken word, but is part of the sentence, it is possible for it to go *outside* the speech marks.
Example:

The teacher asked, "Can you come?"

Why did the teacher say, "You can come"?

Notice the different position of the question mark in each of the examples above.

If words are quoted within the spoken words, these are enclosed in double speech marks if the author has used single speech marks for the words actually spoken, or single ones if he has used double speech marks.
Example:

'Why did the teacher say, "You can come"?' asked Anne.

or "Why did the teacher say, 'You can come'?" asked Anne.

Again, note the position of the question mark in this sentence.

The final point you need to know about writing speech is that every time a new speaker begins to speak, you must begin a new paragraph.

---

### NEW SPEAKER   NEW PARAGRAPH

---

This new line will be indented.

Example:
    "I don't care!" said Michael. "Go without me if you want."
    "Okay, we'll do that!" retorted Beth and slammed the door loudly behind her.
    "I do wish you two would learn to get on," observed Mother, who was washing the dishes.
    "Never!" retaliated Michael. "How can you expect me to even *like* my sister!"

# PRACTICE : DIRECT SPEECH

---

**In DIRECT SPEECH:**

1. **Speech marks are always used in pairs.**
2. **Only words actually spoken are enclosed in speech marks.**
3. **The punctuation of the sentence being spoken remains unchanged and goes inside the speech marks.**
4. **The first word spoken always begins with a capital letter.**
5. **There is always a comma in front of the opening pair of speech marks.**
6. **There is always a punctuation mark at the end of the words spoken. This can be an exclamation mark, question mark or a full stop. However, when narration continues the full stop changes to a comma.**
7. **If narration continues with *he said* (or similar), the first letter of *he* is a small letter (even when this follows a question or exclamation mark belonging to the words spoken).**
8. **If the question or exclamation mark is not part of the spoken words, but part of the sentence, it may go outside the speech marks.**
9. **If words are quoted within the speech marks, single quotation marks are used when the speech marks are double, and vice versa.**
10. **Whenever a new speaker begins to speak, begin a new paragraph.**

**There are three patterns of speech.**

---

**Exercise Four:** _____

Rewrite these sentences inserting speech marks and any other punctuation (including capital letters and final punctuation marks) that is necessary. In each case say which pattern of direct speech is being used. Write your answer, 1, 2 or 3, in the brackets at the end of each sentence.
Example:
               Please lay the table said mother.
          "Please lay the table," said mother.  (_1_)

1.  I think she said I prefer the green one                              (___)

2.  Do you come here often he asked                                 (___)

3. She asked can I have a bowl of soup please      (___)

4. Don't do that shrieked the man      (___)

5. After dinner said Paul we'll go for a walk      (___)

6. I shall miss you when you've gone whispered James      (___)

7. When are we going to the cinema Jade asked      (___)

8. Are you coming Dale snapped or shall I go without you      (___)

9. I think said Barry I'll take the dog for a walk      (___)

10. Can we go to the park now Jenny enquired Liam      (___)

## Exercise Five: _____

Do as you did in Exercise Four above.

1. Do you like my new dress Sandra enquired excitedly      (___)

2. Move further inside please shouted the bus conductor      (___)

3. How are you today asked the young man      (___)

4. I saw you take those sweets said the store manager      (___)

5. Please said the school boy politely take my place      (___)

6. Do you think this colour suits me enquired Jessy      (___)

7. Edward picked up the kitten and said can I have this one please      (___)

8. Look out yelled the foreman watch your head      (___)

9. I'll have steak and chips please said Bernard and an ice cream to follow      (___)

10. It's raining observed the old man and I've left my umbrella at home      (___)

## Exercise Six: _____  _____

The sentences below are written in *REPORTED SPEECH*. Read back through the notes on Reported Speech and then rewrite each sentence in *DIRECT SPEECH* adding all the punctuation marks that are necessary and taking particular care with the tense of the spoken verb.
The number in the brackets next to the sentence identifies the *pattern of speech* you should adopt for your answer.
Example:

He said (that) he was hungry. (_1_)

He said, "I am hungry."

1.   David said that he must go home now.                                      (_2_)

2.   The manager said that there are thirty people waiting outside in the rain.   (_3_)

3.   My friend said that he might be able to come.                             (_1_)

4.   The fat lady said that she loved chocolate cake.                          (_2_)

5.   The twins said that their dog was the best.                              (_1_)

6.   The referee said that we would meet at the stadium the following Saturday.  (_2_)

7.   The caretaker shouted at the boys to close the door.                     (_1_)

8.   I asked Patrick what he wanted.                                         (_2_)

9.   The P.E. teacher asked who would be in the hockey team the following day.  (_3_)

10.  Josie promised not to be late.                                         (_1_)

# THE SEMI-COLON

There are two characteristics of a semi-colon which always apply:

**The semi-colon links two groups of words which are very closely related to each other. Each group of words could easily stand as a sentence in its own right, that is, make complete sense by itself.**

A semi-colon designates a longer pause than a comma, is more forceful than a comma but is not as final as a full stop. By using a semi-colon instead of a full stop suggests an idea is continuing thereby maintaining the flow of thought.

The second group of words is closely related to the first group of words and may provide:
> 1. **more information** about the first group of words,
> 2. **the result** of the first part,
> 3. **the cause** of the first part.

Example:
> She read the book; it was a romantic novel.

Here the second group of words is telling us **more about** the first group of words.

> The baby was screaming loudly; her face was red and puffed.

Here the second group of words tells us **the result** of the baby's screaming.

> He fell heavily onto the running track; he had badly sprained his ankle.

Here the second part tells us **the cause** of his fall.

It is important to note that in each of the examples above the semi-colon separates two groups of words each of which could stand as a sentence in its own right.

He fell heavily onto the running track. He had badly sprained his ankle.

Each part could be written as a separate sentence. The fact that the second part tells us **the cause** of the first part, suggests they could be joined together by a semi-colon. The semi-colon, if you like, emphasises the connection.

**1. A semi-colon can be used between clauses of a compound sentence in place of a conjunction which is ommitted, or,**
**2. when the clauses themselves contain commas.**

Example:
The job had to be finished on time; we thought Jo was the one to do it, but he was not available.
    He fell heavily onto the running track *because* he had sprained his ankle.
    He fell heavily onto the running track; he had sprained his ankle.

In the first example above, the semi-colon splits two clauses the second of which contains commas.

The second example is written with the conjunction *because* (the cause of) *instead of* using a semi-colon.

This would **not** be correct:

He fell heavily onto the running track; because he had sprained his ankle.

The second part here is not a complete sentence and cannot therefore be joined to the first part with a semi-colon. To write *because* **and** use a semi-colon is incorrect. To use a semi-colon **or** a conjunction is correct. Essentially, the semi-colon is taking the place of the conjunction, *because*.

**3. A semi-colon separates items in a list when these are phrases, often themselves containing commas, rather than single words.**

Example:
There was a herbaceous border full of phlox, delphinium, and potentilla; an alpine garden with saxifrage, thyme and candytuft; and at the furthest point, a spectacular wall of broom, rhododendron, clematis and other flowering shrubs.

When a list is simple, the comma is the preferred punctuation mark. However, in more complicated lists, where the items listed may themselves be grouped together, the semi-colon can be used.

# PRACTICE : THE SEMI-COLON

The Semi-colon links two groups of words which are very closely related to each other. Each group of words could easily stand as a sentence in its own right, that is, make complete sense by itself.

The second group of words may provide:
- **a. more information** about the first part,
- **b. the result** of the first part,
- **c. the cause** of the first part.

Use a semi-colon:
1. **Between clauses of a compound sentence in place of a conjunction.**
2. **Between clauses of a compound sentence when the clauses themselves contain commas.**
3. **To separate a list when these are phrases often containing commas, rather than single words.**

**Exercise Seven:** _____

There are ten pairs of sentences in this Exercise. Each pair of sentences has been joined together using a conjunction. Rewrite each pair replacing the conjunction with a semi-colon. Check that each side of the semi-colon can stand as a sentence in its own right.
Example:

|              | He put down his pencil because he had written enough. |
|--------------|-------------------------------------------------------|
| can be rewritten: | He put down his pencil; he had written enough.     |

1.  Sara watched television after she had finished her homework.

2.  The baby was crying because he was hungry.

3.  The old man shivered violently because it was bitterly cold.

4.  Mum told him to brush his hair which was a total mess.

5.  She read the book which was an adventure story.

6.  The children went home tired and hungry because they had had enough.

7.  I shall take some of the library books back now but the others will have to wait.

8.  She had worked very hard for the exam and she hoped it would be enough.

9.  It was a warm, sunny day so they decided to go to the seaside.

10. The parcel had been badly wrapped and some of the contents were showing.

# THE COLON

The colon has quite a definite and different function to a semi-colon and should not be confused with it.

A colon marks a greater degree of separation than does a comma or semi-colon.

**1. A colon is used to show that there is something else to follow, often a list, an example or a piece of speech. A colon is used to direct attention to matter that comes next in the sentence.**

Example:

         These were Julius Caesar's final words: "Et tu Brute?"

Here speech is following the colon.

Example:

     Sally enjoyed lots of pastimes: hockey, netball, rounders, reading, Girl Guides and camping.

     David took everything he needed to camp: a stove, a tent, a sleeping bag, pans and cutlery, matches and a penknife.

Here a list is following the colon.

The first group of words makes a statement about something often by way of a summary. The group of words following the colon gives us more information about that statement, often in the form of a list. Commas can then be used to separate the items listed.

**2. A colon can also introduce a phrase that sums up the point of the sentence. It can be thought of as replacing a word such as *namely*.**

Example:

     There are two qualities I cannot tolerate in a person: laziness and rudeness.

         The solution was obvious: get out.

**3. A colon can be used to balance one thought, idea or phrase against another.**

Example:

Red sky in the morning, shepherd's warning: red sky at night, shepherd's delight.

## PRACTICE : THE COLON

> **1. A colon is used to show that there is something else to follow, often a list, an example, or a piece of speech. A colon is used to direct attention to matter that comes next in the sentence.**
> **2. A colon can introduce a phrase that sums up the point of the sentence. It can be thought of as replacing a word such as *namely*.**
> **3. A colon can be used to balance one thought, idea or phrase against another.**

**Exercise Eight:**_____

Write out the following sentences adding a colon in the correct place. No other punctuation is necessary.

1.  After the match the stadium was covered with rubbish cigarette packets, beer cans, programmes, newspapers, take-away food wrapping and tickets.

2.  There are four varieties of tree in the wood oak, ash, horsechestnut and sycamore.

3.  As I left the house mum said just three words "Do your best".

4.  There are three things about her dog I cannot bear it smells, it sheds hair, it barks.

5.  The results of my examinations were disastrous I failed.

6.  You need to bring some things with you a pencil, a ruler, paper and a ring-binder.

7.  I remember Martin Luther King's words "I have a dream".

8.  There were many things in the cupboard a pair of gloves, a scarf and a handbag.

9.  Three painters represent the Impressionist school of painting Monet, Renoir and Cezanne.

10. A truss is a measure of weight for two things hay and straw.

# BRACKETS

**Brackets ( ), often called *parentheses*, are always used in pairs.**
**They contain information which could easily be left out of a sentence and**
**the sentence make perfectly good sense without it.**

The information in the brackets is *extra* information, less important information, *an aside*, supplementary information, which is not part of the main meaning of the sentence. By using brackets, this less important information is kept out of the way, enabling the reader to fully concentrate upon the main idea of the sentence.
Example:

James used his pocket money (£5) to buy a book.

We'll buy tickets for the cinema (£2 each) and meet you outside at 6 o'clock.

In both these examples, the information in the brackets is not absolutely necessary and is not part of the main meaning of the sentence. In both cases this *extra* information, *hidden away* in brackets, could be left out and the sentences would make perfectly good sense without it.

In this respect, brackets are similar to a pair of commas which is used to separate groups of words which are not absolutely necessary to the meaning of the sentence, that simply add a bit of *extra* information. Indeed there are many occasions when either brackets or commas could be used.

Example:

> Caroline (Captain of the school hockey team) is my best friend.
> Caroline, Captain of the school hockey team, is my best friend.

The effect is the same – to add a bit of *extra* information which is not absolutely necessary to the meaning of the sentence. In both cases, the information could be left out completely and the sentence still make complete sense.

Is there any difference between brackets and commas?
Can I use brackets instead of commas and vice versa?
The answer is yes, on the whole, it is up to you. However, there are some differences:

**a. Information in brackets tends to be a little more *hidden away* than the information between the commas.**

**b. Information in brackets can be used to highlight, explain or exemplify something and in so doing breaks away from the *flow* of the sentence.**

Example:

> For homework, read Chapter Two (pages 6 to 14).
> William Shakespeare (1564 - 1616) was an English dramatist and poet.
> The flowers this year (geraniums, fuschia and delphiniums) are splendid.

As a rule, if the enclosed information does not naturally fit into the main flow of the words of the sentence, use brackets and not commas.

Points to remember when using brackets:

**1. Always use a *pair* of brackets.** If you open a pair of brackets, do not forget to close it!

**2. When the brackets occur in the same place as a punctuation mark belonging to the main sentence, that punctuation mark always comes *after* the second bracket.**

Example:

> Don't forget to take with you some money (£5), some books (library books) and some sweets (chewy ones).

**3. Begin the first word inside the brackets with a capital letter only when the brackets contain a complete sentence standing by itself. A full stop belonging to this sentence would go inside the final bracket.**

Example:

> The paperboy delivered our newspapers to the wrong house last week. (This is the second time he has done that.) Please ensure it does not happen again.

**If the brackets do not contain a complete sentence, begin the first word in the brackets with a small letter.** There is no need to end these words with a full stop although you may use a question or exclamation mark if you choose.

The paperboy (a student, I think) delivered our papers to the wrong address last week.
The paperboy (isn't he tall?) is called Michael.

## PRACTICE : BRACKETS

> **Brackets ( ), often called *parentheses*, are always used in pairs.
> They contain information which could easily be left out of a
> sentence and the sentence make perfectly good sense without it.
> Information in brackets can be used to highlight, explain or
> exemplify something and in so doing breaks away from the *flow* of
> the sentence.**

### Exercise Nine: _____

Each of the following sentences contains information which is not essential to the meaning of the
sentence and could be surrounded by a pair of brackets. Write out each sentence adding a pair of
brackets in the correct place. No other punctuation is necessary.

1.  You should have white wine served cold with fish; red wine served at room temperature
    with red meat.

2.  My sister, Sophie, is studying anthropology the science of man at London University.

3.  The English teacher asked us to find the collective term for eggs clutch, scones batch
    and beautiful ladies bevy. I was the only one who knew the answers.

4.  The unit of currency money for Scandinavia is the krone.

5.  The Eiffel Tower 984 feet high is in Paris.

6.  The distance travelled by light in one year about six million million miles is known as a
    'light year'.

7.  Our veterinary surgeon F.R.C.V.S. Fellow of the Royal College of Veterinary Surgeons is
    also our next door neighbour.

8.  There is an anemometer wind-guage in our school garden.

9.  St. Paul's Cathedral built by Sir Christopher Wren is a well-known feature of the
    London skyline.

10. The largest anchor carried by a ship the sheet anchor is used only in an emergency.

# THE DASH

A dash should never be used as a full stop, semi-colon or comma.
A dash has four distinct uses:

**1. Like brackets, use *a pair of dashes* to enclose information which is not
   part of the main meaning of the sentence.**
Example:
> The Gym Club – hope you're fit – will meet at 6.30 p.m. on Thursday.

Often, a pair of brackets could be used instead.
> The Gym Club (hope you're fit) will meet at 6.30 p.m. on Thursday.

A pair of dashes, however, can give a slight sense of *abruptness*. They do not *hide
away* the information quite as well as a pair of brackets.
Example:
> Your Swimming pass – don't forget it – should be shown on admission.
> Your swimming pass (don't forget it) should be shown on admission.

As with brackets, there is no need to begin the first word with a capital letter or end it
with a full stop or other final punctuation mark. It is possible, however, to use a
question mark or an exclamation mark at the end of the words enclosed by the dashes.
Example:
Laura – do you like the colour of her hair? – is going shopping with me on Saturday.

**2. Use a *single dash* near or at the end of a sentence to summarise or
   emphasise what the author has been saying.**
Example:
> There is only one thing he will object to – noise.

A dash can also be used in this context for a humorous ending.
Example:
> Michael Smith is always invited to all his classmates' homes – once!

In these cases, a colon could be used to *sum up* instead of a dash. However, it would be
wrong to use a comma.

**3. A dash is used to link a series of disconnected phrases.**
Example:
Grandad is my favourite – silver-grey hair – twinkling eyes – kindly smile – gentle
and kind.

**4. In direct speech, *a single dash* is used to show a speaker has changed his
   mind about what he is going to say. Several dashes may be used, if the
   speaker changes his mind several times.**

Example:
"I hope you don't mind – er, I mean I hope you don't want – er, I mean – you're very welcome."

# PRACTICE : THE DASH

A dash has four distinct uses:
1. **Like brackets, a *pair* of dashes is used to enclose information which is not part of the main meaning of the sentence.**
   A pair of dashes gives a slight sense of *abruptness*.
   They do not *hide away* the information quite as well as a pair of brackets.
2. **Use a *single dash* near or at the end of a sentence to summarise or emphasise what the author has been saying.**
3. **A dash is used to link a series of disconnected phrases.**
4. **In direct speech, *a single dash* is used to show a speaker has changed his mind about what he is going to say. Several dashes may be used, if the speaker changes his mind several times.**

**Exercise Ten:** _____

Write out the following sentences adding a dash or a pair of dashes, and any other punctuation between the dashes that may be necessary.

1. As soon as the light began to fade that was early because of the low cloud they set off back to base camp.

2. As soon as he got a place at university he worked very hard for that he went to look for a flat.

3. Auntie Babs isn't she marvellous for sixty-five sent me some money for my birthday.

4. "Well you see I mean oh, please come in!"

5. "Walk if you please don't run."

6. Mick Jones, the soccer coach, said that there was only one reason why he had picked Smith for the first eleven to score goals.

7. They all knew why Sissy won first prize she was the best.

8. Good advice to people about to hang-glide don't.

9. She revved-up the car was she late and screeched out of the drive.

10. Christine told her mother what she wanted for Christmas a computer.

# THE HYPHEN

A hyphen is a shorter line than a dash.
A hyphen has three main functions.

## 1. Use a hyphen between syllables of a word split between two consecutive lines of writing.

Use a hyphen to link two parts of a word together when there is not enough space to finish the word at the end of a line of writing.

1. A hyphen must be placed between two syllables, or between two sounds. It cannot be placed just anywhere in the word. Separate words where the natural pronunciation divides – say sta-tion, not stat-ion. Split between double letters lad-der. Never divide words of one syllable.

2. The hyphen should come at the end of the line on which the split word occurs to show the reader the word is incomplete. It should never come at the beginning of the next line.

Example:
In his study he had many unusual things: an antique desk with brass handles, a bookcase filled with books bound in leather, an old pen, an old grandfather clock and a magnificent leather chair.

Here the word *handles* will not fit onto the first line of writing. To show this word is incomplete, a hyphen is placed after the first syllable of the word (or sound), and the word is continued on the next line. This occurs again with the word *grandfather* on the second line.

## 2. Use a hyphen to separate the parts of some compound words.

Often words are created by joining two or more words together to make a compound word. These compound words are usually linked together with a hyphen.
Example:

The bird-bath in the garden was moss-covered.

Cacti thrive in a well-drained soil.

The student is a hard-working book-lover who should do well.

The arrow was well-aimed. It reached its target with precision.

Some compound words no longer have a hyphen. Words which existed by themselves originally were brought together with a hyphen to form a new word. In time, these words have lost their hyphen and are now commonplace.
Example:

news + agent = news-agent = newsagent

wall + paper = wall-paper = wallpaper

**3. A hyphen can be used to link the words of a phrase.**
Example:

> The Morris Dancers seemed to weave in-and-out and round-and-round.
> The boy had an unfortunate couldn't-care-less attitude which spoilt him.

Be careful! Make sure you hyphenate everything that should be hyphenated, otherwise silly mistakes can be made!
Example:

> Jane is in a class of ten-year-old girls. (Everyone is ten.)

is quite a different prospect to:

> Jane is in a class of ten year-old girls. (Ten children, each one year old!)

Other uses include:
**A. To create a special effect.**
Example:

> Speak s-l-o-w-l-y and c-l-e-a-r-l-y so the old lady understands.

**B. To avoid ambiguity.**
To distinguish between two words which have identical sounds and spellings but which have quite different meanings.
Example:
We asked him to resign last week. Now we are asking him to re-sign his contract!

**C. Words beginning with the word *self*, *well* or a *number* are often hyphenated.**
Example:

> Michael is a *self*-confident, *well*-mannered *fifth*-form pupil.

**D. Many words with prefixes such as *pre-*, *pro-* and *non-* are also hyphenated.**
Example:

> Spain used to be a *non*-EEC country.     In *post*-war Britain...
> She is a *post*-graduate...                        *Pre*-tax profits this year...

**E. A hyphen is used to separate two vowels which occur together in a word but which are pronounced separately.**
Example:

> co-operate

# PRACTICE : THE HYPHEN

> A hyphen is a shorter line that a dash. A hyphen has three main functions.
>
> 1. **Use a hyphen between syllables of a word split between two consecutive lines of writing.**
> 2. **Use a hyphen to separate the parts of some compound words.**
> 3. **A hyphen can be used to link the words of a phrase.**

---

Other uses include:

A. **To create a special effect.**
B. **To avoid ambiguity.**
C. **Words beginning with** *self, well* **or a** *number* **are often hyphenated.**
D. **Many words with prefixes such as** *pre-, pro-* **and** *non-*
   **are also hyphenated.**
E. **A hyphen is used to separate two vowels which occur**
   **together in a word but which are pronounced separately.**

---

**Exercise Eleven:** _____

Each of the following sentences contains words which should be joined together by a hyphen. Write out each sentence adding a hyphen in the correct place.

1. The bird bath in the garden is moss covered.

2. At school Sally is in a class of thirty ten year olds.

3. The pink coloured azalea in the pretty bowl was presented as first prize at the gymkhana.

4. The well aimed arrow hit the target with precision and scored full marks.

5. "I hope you will co operate with me," said Miss Jones.

6. John is a self motivated, well mannered and self confident third form student who should do well.

7. The tickets were pre booked.

8. Non payment will result in further action.

9. The lesson lasted for one and a half hours.

10. The music played at three quarter time.

## INVERTED COMMAS

Like speech marks, inverted commas(' ') are written in pairs. However, unlike speech marks which can be pairs of *double* or *single* raised commas, inverted commas are only *single* raised commas.

**1. Inverted commas are used to surround the titles of books, films, plays, television programmes etc.**

Punctuation marks which are a part of the sentence and do not belong to the title go outside the inverted commas.
Example:
The four tragedies of Shakespeare are 'Macbeth', 'Hamlet', 'Orthello' and 'King Lear'.

**2. Inverted commas are also used to enclose words you wish to emphasise or stress, words of slang, irony or words expressed as a joke.**
Example:

What is meant by 'resilient'?
It rained every day during what were supposed to be our 'summer' holidays.

Words of slang remain words of slang and the author cannot give them respectability by enclosing them in inverted commas. Avoid using words of slang in any written piece of work except where they add colour and interest to the speech of a character, or a style.

# PRACTICE : INVERTED COMMAS

---

Inverted commas are a pair of *single* raised commas.
They have two main functions:
1.   **To surround the titles of books, films, plays, television programmes etc.**
2.   **To enclose words you wish to emphasise or stress, words of slang, irony or words expressed as a joke.**

---

**Exercise Twelve:** _____

Write out the sentences below inserting the inverted commas correctly.

1.   Shaun agreed that the film version of Jurassic Park was better than the book.

2.   For many years the chair person of Question Time was Sir Robin Day.

3.   "Open, Sesme!" were the magic words used in Ali Baba and the Forty Thieves.

4.   Sara went to Stratford-Upon-Avon to see Midsummer Night's Dream, her favourite play.

5.   David has just finished reading Robinson Crusoe by Daniel Defoe.

6.   Neighbours, Home and Away and Grangehill are Michael's favourite television programmes.

7.   Sara so enjoyed reading Redwall, Mossflower and Salamandastron, that now she is in the bookshop looking for Mattimeo by the same author, Brian Jacques.

8.  You've Been Framed, Blind Date and Crystal Maze are James' favourite T.V. programmes.

9.  Witches, The Magic Finger and Matilda are just three of the novels of Roald Dahl.

10. As part of our studies of First World War poets, we are looking at Rupert Brooke's, The Soldier.

# QUOTATION MARKS

**Quotation marks are pairs of double raised commas (" ").**
**When quoting directly from a piece of literature, or exact words spoken, it is necessary to enclose the precise words quoted in a pair of quotation marks.**

When it is necessary to quote from another text, there are certain rules that must be obeyed.

When quoting poetry or prose:
**1. If you are quoting less that one line of verse of poetry or prose, or less than one sentence spoken, the quoted words can form part of the normal sentence enclosing the words quoted in quotation marks.**
Example:
"Into the valley of death rode the six hundred" is a famous quote from Tennyson's 'Charge of the Light Brigade'.

**2. If you are quoting more than one line of verse or prose, start the quotation on a new line and write the quote as lines of a verse with short or half lines in the same place as the original version. To show precisely what has been quoted, start all lines of the passage slightly indented from the left-hand margin. Quotation marks are not used. When the quotation is complete, begin a new line at the left-hand side of the page.**
Example:
Upon receiving news of the imminence of the Spanish Armada, Sir Francis Drake, enjoying a game of bowls said:

> There's plenty of time to finish this game and thrash the Spaniards too.

And that he proceeded to do!

**3. If more than a paragraph is quoted, quotation marks are used at the beginning of each paragraph but not at the end, except for the final paragraph.**

**4. If direct speech forms part of the quotation, use single inverted commas to surround the words spoken.**
Example:
Churchill said on 13th May, 1940: "I will say to this House, as I have said to those who joined this Government: 'I have nothing to offer but blood, toil, tears and sweat.' "

# PRACTICE : QUOTATION MARKS

> **When quoting directly from a piece of literature, or exact words spoken, it is necessary to enclose the precise words quoted in a pair of quotation marks.**
> **Quotation marks are pairs of double raised commas (" ").**

## Exercise Thirteen: _____

A quote is given to you and underneath a sentence written about it.
Place quotation marks correctly where necessary in those following sentences.

*Who will free me from this turbulent priest?*
1. When Henry ll described Beckett as this turbulent priest of whom he wished to be free, he did not realise that his faithful followers would indeed carry out his wishes and murder Beckett.

*England is a nation of shopkeepers.*
2. Napoleon disparagingly describes England as a nation of shopkeepers.

*Eureka!*
3. Archimedes, as he stepped into his bath, noticed the displaced water overflowing, and is said to have exclaimed, Eureka!  Archimedes Principle was discovered.

*Veni, vidi, vici.*
4. I came, I saw, I conquered: Veni, vidi, vici, is the famous quotation of Julius Caesar on conquering Britain.

*I like work; it fascinates me. I can sit and look at it for hours.*
5. I like work; it fascinates me. I can sit and look at it for hours, is a quotation by Jerome K. Jerome.

# THE APOSTROPHE

An apostrophe is a small raised comma which has two functions:

　　1. To show possession
　　2. In a contraction

In both cases the apostrophe shows that something has been left out.
This could be the word *of* when we are talking about *the ownership of something*, or a letter or group of letters in the case of a *contraction*.

## 1. The Apostrophe used to show *Ownership*

When an apostrophe is used to show the ownership of something, it takes the place of the word *of*. The small raised comma either precedes an *s* or comes immediately after an *s* which is added to the end of a word.
Example:

|  |  |
| --- | --- |
|  | The books of the girls. |
| could be rewritten | The girls' books. |
|  |  |
|  | The kittens of the cat |
| could be rewritten | The cat's kittens. |

**In both cases the apostrophe takes the place of the word *of* and goes before or after an *s* which is added to the end of the word.**

**A word ends is *'s* or *s'* to show that it is the owner of whatever immediately follows.**

---

To decide where to put the apostrophe ask:

1.    **WHO IS THE OWNER?**
2.    **Place the apostrophe immediately after the answer.**

---

If we look at the two examples above:

The books of the girls.

and ask *WHO owns the books?*

The answer is:          The girls (plural).

*Place the apostrophe immediately after the answer.*
This then becomes:          The girls' books.

---

**When the owner is plural the apostrophe follows the s (s').**

---

The kittens of the cat.

*WHO owns the kittens?*
Answer:          The cat (singular).

*Place the apostrophe immediately after the answer.*
Becomes:          The cat's kittens.

---

**When the owner is singular the apostrophe precedes the s ('s).**

---

There are two important points concerning the apostrophe.

**1. If the owner's name already ends in *s* there is no need to add another *s*, simply add the apostrophe.**

Example:

> The boat of Mr Williams.

Becomes:

> Mr Williams' boat.

Similarly, when the noun is plural and therefore ends in *s*, add the apostrophe only.

Example:

> The tails of the horses.

Becomes:

> The horses' tails.

**2. If a noun changes completely in the plural, treat the word as if it were singular, and place the apostrophe before the s ('s).**

Some words change completely in the plural.

Example:

| | | |
|---|---|---|
| child | becomes | children |
| tooth | becomes | teeth |
| man | becomes | men |

When adding an apostrophe to these words, treat them as though they were singular and place the apostrophe before the s ('s).

Example:

> The toys of the children

Becomes:

> The children's toys.
>
> The bags of the women.

Becomes:

> The women's bags.

In fact, if you always apply the two Rules:

1. Ask: WHO IS THE OWNER?

2. Always place the apostrophe immediately after the answer.

Then you should never have any difficulty placing an apostrophe accurately.

Special cases:

In compound words and two words showing a joint possession, only the last word uses the apostrophe.

Example:

> This is my son-in-law's house.
>
> Jason and Mary's mother is coming to school.

## PRACTICE : AN APOSTOPHE TO SHOW OWNERSHIP

An apostrophe is a small raised comma which has two functions:

> **A.** **To show ownership.**
>
> **B.** **In a contraction.**

**In both cases the apostrophe shows that something has been left out. This could be the word *of* when we are talking about *the ownership of something*, or a letter or group of letters in the case of a *contraction*.**

### A. TO SHOW OWNERSHIP
To decide where to put the apostrophe ask:
1. **Who is the owner?**
2. **Place the apostrophe immediately after the answer.**

A. **A word ends is 's or s' to show that it is the *owner of whatever immediately follows it*.**
   **When the owner is *plural* the apostrophe follows the s (s').**
   **When the owner is *singular* the apostrophe precedes the s ('s).**
B. **If the owner's name already ends in *s* there is no need to add another *s*, simply *add the apostrophe*.**
C. **If a noun changes completely in the plural, treat the word as if it were *singular*, and place the apostrophe *before the s ('s)*.**

Special cases:
**In compound words and two words showing a joint possession, only the *final* word uses the apostrophe.**

## Exercise Fourteen: _____

Rewrite the following groups of words adding the apostrophe in the correct place.

1. The childrens toys

2. Mr Williams boat

3. The ladies hats

4. James toy train set

5. Saras mountain bike

6. The teams score

7. The boats crew

8. The books cover

9. The son-in-laws mother

10. The newsagents shop

## Exercise Fifteen: _____

This time, the phrases contain the word *of*. Rewrite these groups of words leaving out the word *of* and placing an apostrophe in the correct place.

1. The hats of Mrs Jones and Mrs Williams

2.  The bags of the students

3.  The leaves of the trees

4.  The leaves of the tree

5.  The father of Jade and Liam

6.  The whiskers of the cat

7.  The sister of James

8.  The glances of the passers-by

9.  The edge of the pavement

10. The scissors of the hairdresser

# AN APOSTROPHE IN A CONTRACTION

When we speak we often run words together and in so doing, omit letters or groups of letters. This short way of writing is called a *contraction*.

---

**In a contraction, an apostrophe is used where the letters are missing.**

---

Example:

|            | can be shortened to |          |
|------------|---------------------|----------|
| could not  |                     | couldn't |
| they are   |                     | they're  |

In both these cases the words are joined together and the apostrophe is inserted in the exact place of the missing letter - the *o* in *not*, and the *a* in *are*.
Take care! When we use *its*, meaning *belonging to it* (a possessive pronoun), there is no apostrophe. Similarly there is no apostrophe with other possessive pronouns such as *hers*, *his*, *ours*, *yours* and *theirs*.
Only when we write *it is* in its shortened form do we use an apostrophe.
Example:

> The dog is wagging its tail.
> It's a lovely, sunny day.

Over the decades words such as influenza, perambulator, telephone and omnibus have been shortened to form the familiar words *flu*, *pram*, *phone* and *bus*. To be correct, these words should have apostrophes. Modern usage, however, has dictated these apostrophes are no longer necessary.

# PRACTICE : AN APOSTROPHE IN A CONTRACTION

---

**B. IN A CONTRACTION**
**In a contraction, an apostrophe is used where the letter or letters are missing.**
When we use *its* meaning *belonging to it* (a possessive pronoun), there is no apostrophe.

---

**Exercise Sixteen:** _____

Rewrite each sentence below. Place an apostrophe exactly where a letter or letters has been omitted in the words which have been run together.

1. If youre ready to go, well leave. I thought wed go swimming.

2. Its a lovely day. I thought wed go for a walk. You can come, cant you?

3. The cat is licking its paw. I think its hurt it. Well have to take it to the vet.

4. Wont you turn down that radio? Ive had about as much as I can take.

5. Dont do that! Weve waited a long time for his call and if you lift the receiver he wont get through.

6. She hasnt got your tea ready because she wasnt expecting you until later.

7. It isnt fair. You went first last time. Its my turn.

8. Couldnt we wait just a little longer? Hes probably rushing to us now.

9. Hows your father? I hear hes been unwell. I hope hes better soon.

10. Theres always a second chance, so dont give up all the hard work. Its worth it in the end.

# THE PARAGRAPH

A sentence is a group of words which makes complete sense by itself. It is an expression of a single, complete and coherent idea. It begins with a capital letter and ends with a full stop, exclamation or question mark. Each sentence usually consists of a subject and predicate containing a finite verb. The full stop is the strongest punctuation mark in a sentence.

A paragraph is a collection of several sentences which are grouped or linked together because they relate to the same main topic or idea. Everything in that paragraph then relates to this main topic. A paragraph has unity.

When planning a piece of fiction it is often an idea to jot down *topic sentences* in the same sequence as the story. Each *topic sentence* contains the central idea of the paragraph and is often the first sentence of a paragraph. More sentences, which enlarge and enhance each topic, are then added to these *topic sentences*. Each *topic sentence* together with its subordinate sentences, becomes a paragraph. For the reader, this *topic sentence* tells him what the paragraph is about. Everything in that paragraph then relates to this main topic. Then, as the reader begins each new paragraph, he is beginning to read about a new aspect of the topic. In this way even the most formidable piece of writing is broken up into easily digestible chunks and the reader is taken through a piece of writing in a clear and easy-to-follow manner.

The mechanics of paragraphing is easy. There are two characteristics of a paragraph.

1. Each new paragraph begins a new line.
2. The first word of the paragraph is indented away from the left-hand margin.

There is no set length to a paragraph which may be considered *a unit of thought* rather than *a unit of length.*

Finally, when there is direct speech in an essay, remember:
For each new speaker begin a new paragraph.

# RULE SUMMARIES

Here you are asked to do three things:
1.  Read through all the Rules that have been identified in this book, one at a time.
2.  When you are ready, fill in the missing words in the Rule Summaries below.
3.  Explain in your own words what is meant by each Rule, making reference to the examples given.

# DIRECT AND REPORTED SPEECH

Read through the Exercises and notes on **DIRECT AND REPORTED SPEECH** on page 1 and when you are ready complete the following Rule Summary without referring to that section.

Actual words spoken by someone is called _____ _____.
Speech marks, or _____ _____, are used to enclose the actual words spoken.
Reported or _____ _____ is not spoken. It is a _____ of what was spoken.
Reported speech does not contain _____ \_\_\_\_\_.

Now turn back to page 1 and check your answer.

### KEEPING YOUR OWN RECORD OF THE PUNCTUATION RULES IN THESE BOOKS

To keep a permanent record of the Punctuation Rules in these books - a record to which you can refer at any time - you need a pack of 5ins x 8ins index cards and an index card box or A5 file. You have already made ten Record Cards from *Punctuation Rules and Practice 1*. Continue here with Card Eleven.

## CARD ELEVEN:
Copy the summary concerning **DIRECT and REPORTED SPEECH** from page 1 carefully and clearly onto the first side of Card Eleven. Spread out your writing so it is neat and easy to read.

On the reverse of Card Eleven give two examples of direct speech and two examples of indirect, or reported speech.

## CARD TWELVE and THIRTEEN:
Read through the notes concerning **REPORTED SPEECH** on pages 2 to 6, and when you are ready, complete the following Rule Summary without referring to those pages.

## In **REPORTED SPEECH:**
1. A _____ word such as *that* is usually used except when the word following is
   the _____, in which case *that* can be omitted.
2. The _____ of the verb may change.
   When the words are spoken *in the present*,
   the tense of the *spoken verb*:
       a. *moves back in time* when a *past* _____ verb is used.
       b. *remains the same* when a *present* _____ verb is used.
   When the words were spoken *in the past*,
   the tense of the *spoken verb*:
       c. either *moves back* still further, or *remains* \_\_\_\_ _____
   The tense may not _____ if the what is true when the words are spoken in direct
   speech remains _____ when the words are reported.

When there is a difference between what is true and what is _____, the tense of the verb changes.

3. Personal and possessive pronouns:
   pronouns in the _____ person are changed to pronouns in the _____ person (singular or plural).
4. Places and _____ often change.
5. Question words in direct speech _____ in reported speech. Where there is no question word use ____ or _____.
   The auxiliary verb ____, _____, _____ is not used in reported questions.
6. Change a command into the _____ of the verb.
7. Where is command or _____ is in the negative, use *not to* with the _____.

Turn to page 6 and correct your answers. Copy the Rule Summaries concerning **REPORTED SPEECH** neatly and clearly onto both sides of Card Twelve.


Onto Card Thirteen:
1. Explain what is meant by a *connecting word* and when it may be omitted.
2. Give examples to illustrate the changing tense of the *spoken* verb when a present and a past *reporting* verb is used. Show how the tense of the *spoken* verb changes each time. Explain how a spoken verb already in the past may change or may remain the same. Give examples to show this.
3. Explain, giving examples, why *I* changes to *him*, *her* or *it*, and *we* changes to *their*. Similarly, the possessive pronouns change. Say how, and give examples.
4. Show how places and times change.
5. Show, by example, how a question word may be retained, and what alternative there is when a question word is not included in the direct speech.
6. Give examples to show the disappearance of the auxiliary verb *do*, *does* or *did*.
7. Give examples to show the use of the infinitive of the verb in a. a command, and b.when a command or promise is in the negative.


## CARD FOURTEEN:
Read pages 8 to 12 concerning **DIRECT SPEECH** and when you are ready complete the following Rule Summaries without reference to those pages.


Whenever you are writing the _____ words _____ by someone, you are writing DIRECT SPEECH. In Direct speech a pair of _____ marks must be used. These may look like this (___) or this (_____).
1. Speech marks are always used in _____.
2. Only words _____ _____ are enclosed in speech marks.
3. The punctuation of the sentence being spoken remains _____ and goes _____ the speech marks.
4. The first word actually spoken always begins with a _____ _____.
5. There is always a _____ in front of the opening pair of speech marks.
6. There is always a _____ mark at the end of the words spoken.
   This can be an _____ mark, _____ mark or a full stop. However, when narration continues, the full stop changes to a _____.
7. If narration continues with *he said*, the first letter of *he* is a _____ _____, (even when this follows a question or exclamation mark belonging to the words spoken.)

8. If the question or exclamation mark is not part of the spoken words, but part of the sentence, it may go _____ the speech marks.
9. If words are quoted within the speech marks, _____ quotation marks are used when the speech marks are double, and vice versa.
10. Whenever a new speaker begins to speak, begin a _____ _____.

Look back at page 8 and page 12 to correct your answers. Carefully copy the Rule Summaries from page 8 and page 12 taking both sides of Card Fourteen.

## CARD FIFTEEN:
Study the **THREE PATTERNS OF DIRECT SPEECH** and the notes about these three patterns on pages 9 to 11, and when you are ready, complete the following without referring to those pages.

It is possible to identify **THREE PATTERNS of writing DIRECT SPEECH**.

| | |
|---|---|
| 1. | "A_____B " C said. |
| 2. | He said D "E_____ F " |
| 3. | "G__H " he said J "K_____L" |

Key:  CL = capital letter   sl = small letter

Complete the key A to L. (There is no letter I.) Then turn back to page 9 to check your answers. Copy carefully the **Three Patterns of writing Direct Speech** (and key) (as shown on page 9) onto the first side of Card Sixteen.

On the reverse of Card Sixteen:
1. Read through the notes about these three patterns on pages 9 to 11, and when you are ready, list the points (rules) that can be observed (applied) in all three patterns. These are summarised for you on page 11. Give examples to illustrate these points.
2. Discuss in your own words, *the special cases* mentioned on page 11. Give examples.

## CARD SEVENTEEN:
Read about **THE SEMI-COLON** on pages 14 to 16 and when you are ready, complete the following Rule Summary without referring to those pages.

The semi-colon links two groups of words which are _____ _____ _____ to each other. Each group of words could easily stand as a _____ its own right, that is, make complete _____ by itself.
The second group of words may provide:
    a. more _____ about the first part,
    b. the _____ of the first part,
    c. the _____ of the first part.

Use a semi-colon:
1. Between clauses of a compound sentence in place of a _____.

2. Between clauses of a compound sentence when the clauses themselves contain
   _____.

3. To separate a list when these are _____ often containing _____, rather than
   single words.

Turn back to page 16 and correct your answers. Then, copy the Rule Summary from page 16 carefully and neatly onto the first side of Card Seventeen.

On the reverse of Card Seventeen discuss in detail and in your own words, the three uses of the semi-colon as discussed on page 15. Give examples to illustrate the points you are making.

## CARD EIGHTEEN:
Read the notes concerning **THE COLON** on page 17, and when you are ready, complete the following Rule Summary without referring to that page.

1. A colon is used to show that there is something else to follow, often a _____, an
   _____, or a piece of _____.
   A colon is used to direct attention to matter that comes next in the sentence.
2. A colon can also introduce a phrase that _____ _____ the point of the sentence. It
   can be thought of as replacing a word such as _____.
3. A colon can be used to balance one thought, _____ or _____ against another.

Turn back to page 17 and correct your answers. Then, copy carefully and neatly the Rule Summary from page 17 onto the first side of Card Eighteen.

On the reverse of Card Eighteen:
Explain in your own words what each group of words, separated by a colon, is doing:
That the first group of words makes a statement about something often by way of a summary and the second group of words gives us more information about that statement. In what form? Give examples.
With the use of examples, discuss the remaining two uses of the colon.

## CARD NINETEEN:
Read pages 18 to 20 about **BRACKETS**, and when you are ready complete the following Rule Summary without referring to those pages.

Brackets ( ), often called _____, are always used in pairs.
They contain information which could _____ _____ ____ of a sentence and the
sentence make perfectly good sense without it.
Information in brackets can be used to _____, _____ or _____
something and in so doing breaks away from the _____ of the sentence.

Turn back to page20 to check your answers. Copy the Rule Summary from page 20 carefully and neatly onto the first side of Card Nineteen.

On the reverse of Card Nineteen:
1. Explain what sort of information is contained in the brackets.
2. Explain in what way a pair of brackets is similar to a pair of commas. Give examples.
3. Discuss the difference between using commas and using brackets, and when it would be more appropriate to use brackets than commas. What can the information contained in the brackets be used for?
4. Discuss the use of brackets in regard to the punctuation of the sentence.

**CARD TWENTY:**
Read pages 21 and 22 concerning **THE DASH** and then complete the following Rule Summary without referring to those pages.

A dash has _____ distinct uses:
1. Like brackets, a _____ of dashes is used to enclose information which is not part of the main meaning of the sentence. A pair of dashes gives a slight sense of _____. They do not _____ _____ the information quite as well as a pair of brackets.
2. Use a _____ *dash* near or at the _____ of a sentence to summarise or _____ what the author has been saying.
3. A dash is used to link a series of disconnected _____.
4. In direct speech, *a* _____ *dash* is used to show a speaker has changed his _____ about what he is going to say. Several dashes may be used, if the speaker changes his mind several times!

Turn back to page 22 to check your answers. Now copy carefully and clearly, the Rule Summary from page 22 onto the first side of Card Twenty.

On the reverse of that Card:
1. Give examples to show the similarity of a pair of dashes and a pair of brackets. Explain the advantage in using dashes rather than brackets.
2. Discuss the punctuation of the words between the dashes. Give examples of your own to illustrate this.
3. Give examples to show how a dash can be used to summarise or emphasise what the author has been saying.
4. Discuss how a dash can be used to join together a series of disconnected phrases. Give examples.
5. Show the use of the dash in direct speech. That when a speaker changes his mind, a dash can be used.

**CARD TWENTY-ONE:**
Read the notes on pages 23 to 25 about **THE HYPHEN**. Then when you are ready, complete the following Rule Summary without reference to those pages.

A hyphen is a _____ line that a dash.
A hyphen has _____ main functions.
1. Use a hyphen between syllables of a word _____ between two consecutive _____ of writing.
2. Use a hyphen to separate the parts of some _____ words.
3. A hyphen can be used to link the words of a _____.

Other uses include:
A. To create a special _____.
B. To avoid _____.
C. Words beginning with the _____, _____ or a _____ are often hyphenated.
D. Many words with prefixes such as _____, _____ and _____ are also hyphenated.
E. A hyphen is used to separate two _____ which occur together in a word but which are pronounced _____.

Turn back to pages 24 and 25 to check your answers. Then carefully and clearly copy the Rule Summaries on those pages onto the first side of Card Twenty-One.

On the reverse of that Card:

1. Explain in your own words where you would place a hyphen in a word split between two consecutive lines of writing. On which line? Whereabouts in the word? Which words are never split?

2. Explain, giving examples, what is meant by a *compound* word.

3. Give examples of the use of a hyphen to link words of a phrase.

4. Under the side headings of A to D above, give examples of each of the other uses.

## CARD TWENTY-TWO:

Read pages 25 and 26 concerning **INVERTED COMMAS** and when you are ready, complete the following Rule Summary without referring to those pages.

Inverted commas are a pair of _____ raised commas.

They have _____ main functions:

1. To surround the _____ of books, films, plays, television programmes etc.

2. To enclose words you wish to _____ or stress, words of _____, irony or words expressed as a _____.

Turn back to page 26 and correct your answers. Now, copy the Rule Summary on page 26 neatly and carefully onto the first side of Card Twenty-Two. On the reverse of that Card give examples of each part of the Rules above to show the use of inverted commas.

## CARD TWENTY-THREE:

Read page 27 about **QUOTATION MARKS** and when you are ready copy the following Rule Summary onto the first side of Card Twenty-Three.

When quoting directly from a piece of literature, or exact words _____, it is necessary to enclose the precise words quoted in a _____ of _____ marks.

Quotation marks are _____ of double raised commas (    ).

On the reverse of that Card:

1. Explain how you integrate less than one line of verse or prose into the normal sentence and how you show it is a quote. Give an example to demonstrate this.

2. Explain what rules have to be applied when you are quoting more than one line of verse or prose. Give an example to show this.

3. Explain the technique of quoting more than one paragraph of text.

4. Finally, by way of example, show how you deal with direct speech when it forms part of a quotation.

## CARD TWENTY-FOUR:

Read pages 28 to 31 about **THE APOSTROPHE** and when you are ready, complete the following Rule Summary without referring to those pages.

An apostrophe is a small raised comma which has _____ functions:

      A. To show _____

      B. In a _____

In both cases the apostrophe shows that something has been _____ _____.

This could be the word ____ when we are talking about *the* _____ *of something*, or a letter or group of letters in the case of a _____.

## A. TO SHOW OWNERSHIP
To decide where to put the apostrophe ask:

      1. ____ ___ _____ _____?

      2. Place the apostrophe immediately after the _____.

1. A word ends is *'s* or *s'* to show that it is the _____ of whatever immediately _____ it. When the owner is _____ the apostrophe follows the s'. When the owner is _____ the apostrophe precedes the 's.

2. If the owner's name already ends in *s* there is no need to _____ another *s*, simply add the _____.

3. If a noun changes completely in the _____, treat the word as if it were singular, and place the apostrophe _____ the 's.

Special cases:

    In compound words and two words showing a joint possession, only the _____ word uses the apostrophe.

## B. IN A CONTRACTION
In a contraction, an apostrophe is used where the letter or letters are _____.

When we use *its* meaning *belonging to it* (a _____ pronoun), there is no apostrophe.

Turn back to pages 30, 31 and 33 to check your answers. Then copy the above Rule Summaries carefully and neatly onto the first side of Card Twenty-Four.

On the reverse of that Card make notes of your own, together with examples, of any points regarding **THE APOSTROPHE** which you need to remember.

## CARD TWENTY-FIVE:
Make any notes on Card Twenty-Five about **THE PARAGRAPH** which you may find useful to remember.

1. Make a note of what is meant by a *topic sentence*, where this sentence should be in a paragraph and how breaking up a story into topic sentences helps with not only the writing, but also eventually with the reading of a story.

2. What is meant by the sentence: *a paragraph is not so much a unit of length as a unit of thought.*
Explain fully in your own words.

3. Explain the mechanics and the two characteristics of a paragraph.

4. Finally, make a particular note of paragraphing in relation to direct speech.

# A N S W E R S

### Exercise 1

1. The old lady asked Mary to close the door.                    (_R_)
2. You can go now, said the teacher to her class.               (_D_)
3. We are going abroad for our holiday this year,
   said Bernard.                                                 (_D_)
4. Bernard said that he was going abroad for his
   holiday this year.                                            (_R_)
5. She said she would do her homework later.                    (_R_)
6. Hold tight! shouted the bus conductor.                       (_D_)
7. She said she never wanted to see him again.                  (_R_)
8. Why are you late? asked the referee.                         (_D_)
9. The doctor said, Take the medicine twice a day.              (_D_)
10. The athlete wondered why everyone was cheering.             (_R_)

### Exercise 2

1. Barry asked where were they going that day.
   The question word *where* remains (Point 5).
   The personal pronoun *we* changes to *they* (Point 3).
   *are going* changes to *were going* as past reporting verb
   *asked* is used (point 2a).
   *today* becomes *that day* (Point 4).
2. David asks where is the cinema.
   The question word *where* remains (Point 5).
   Present tense in reporting verb *asks* present tense *is*
   remains (Point 2b).
3. The operator said that the number was engaged.
   Connecting word *that* is used (Point 1).
   Past tense in the reporting verb *said* : *is* changes to
   *was* (Point 2a).
4. The boy said that he might be able to go swimming.
   Past reporting verb *said* : - *may* becomes *might* (Point 2a).
   Connecting word *that* (Point 1).
   *I* personal pronoun becomes *he* (Point 3).
5. Maria shouted to Sam to close the door.
   The imperative *close* becomes the infinitive *to close* (Point 6).
6. The teacher asked Barnaby what he wanted.
   Auxiliary verb *do* is not used (Point 5).
   Question word *what* is kept (Point 5).
7. Jack promised not to do that again.
   *Not* with the infinitive of the verb is used in a
   negative promise (or command) (Point 7).
8. Louise said to (told) Robert to come on time.
   The spoken command is changed to the infinitive
   of the verb (to come) (Point 6).
9. Rev. Simms said that they would meet there
   again the following Sunday.
   *We will* changes to *they would* (Point 2a).
   Personal pronoun changes from the first person plural
   to the third person plural (Point 3).
   *next Sunday* becomes the *following Sunday* (Point 4).
   *Here* becomes *there* (Point 4).
10. Timothy said that his brother is eighteen.
    *My brother* becomes *his brother* (Point 3).
    *is* remains if what is true when the words are spoken
    in direct speech remains true when reported (Point 2).

### Exercise 3

1. Mother said (that) they would go to the cinema the
   following day.
   Connecting word *that* can be used (Point 1).
   *shall go* becomes *would go* (Point 2a).
   *Tomorrow* becomes *the following day* (Point 4).
2. The teacher yelled to shut up and (to) sit down.
   The two commands *shut up* and *sit down* change into
   the infinitive *to shut up* and *to sit down* (Point 6).
3. Helen asked Sandra where she lived.
   Question word *where* is retained (Point 5).
   *Do* is dropped (Point 5).
4. Christopher said he might go.
   *May* becomes *might* in the past tense (Point 2a).
   *I* becomes *he* (Point 3).
5. The bronzed youth said (that) he lives in Spain.
   Connecting word *that* may be used (Point 1).
   *Lives* is retained if what is true when the words are spoken
   remains true when the speech is reported (Point 2).
6. Arthur said (that) he had swum (or swam) six
   lengths of the pool that day.
   Connecting word *that* may be used (Point 1).
   *had swum* or *swam* - either is acceptable with
   a past reporting verb (Point 2c).
   *Today* becomes *that day* (Point 4).
7. Cheri said that there are twenty-eight pupils in her class.
   Connecting word *that* (Point 1).
   If what is true when the words are spoken remains
   true when the words are reported *there are* is correct (Point 2).
   *My* becomes *her* (Point 3).
8. The gardener shouted to close that window.
   Imperative becomes the infinitive in reported speech (Point 6).
9. Michael promised not to be long.
   *I* becomes *he* or *Michael* (Point 3).
   A promise in the negative becomes *not* with the infinitive (Pt.7).
10. The old lady asks if I will have a cup of tea.
    Introduce the reported words with *if* or *whether* when there
    is no question word present in the words spoken (Point 5).
    The tense of the verb in the words spoken is not changed
    when a reporting verb in the present tense is used (Point 2b).

### Exercise 4

1. "I think," she said, "I prefer the green one."              (_3_)
2. "Do you come here often?" he asked.                         (_1_)
3. She asked, "Can I have a bowl of soup, please?"            (_2_)
4. "Don't do that!" shrieked the man.                          (_1_)
5. "After dinner," said Paul, "we'll go for a walk."          (_3_)
6. "I shall miss you when you've gone," whispered James.      (_1_)
7. "When are we going to the cinema?" Jade asked.             (_1_)
8. "Are you coming," Dale snapped, "or shall I go without
   you?"                                                       (_3_)
9. "I think," said Barry, "I'll take the dog for a walk."     (_3_)
10. "Can we go to the park now, Jenny?" enquired Liam.        (_1_)

## Exercise 5

1. "Do you like my new dress?" Sandra enquired excitedly. (_1_)
2. "Move further inside, please," shouted the bus conductor. (_1_)
3. "How are you today?" asked the young man. (_1_)
4. "I saw you take those sweets," said the store manager. (_1_)
5. "Please," said the school boy politely, "take my place." (_3_)
6. "Do you think this colour suits me?" enquired Jessy. (_1_)
7. Edward picked up the kitten and said, "Can I have this one, please?" (_2_)
8. "Look out," yelled the foreman, "watch your head!" (_3_)
9. "I'll have steak and chips, please," said Bernard, "and an ice cream to follow." (_3_)
10. "It's raining," observed the old man, "and I've left my umbrella at home." (_3_)

## Exercise 6

1. David said, "I must go home now."
2. "There are," said the manager, "thirty people waiting outside in the rain."
3. "I may be able to come," said my friend.
4. The fat lady said, "I love chocolate cake."
5. "Our dog is the best," said the twins.
6. The referee said, "We will meet at the stadium next Saturday."
7. "Close the door!" shouted the caretaker at the boys.
8. I asked, "What do you want, Patrick?"
9. "Who," asked the P.E. teacher, "will be in the hockey team tomorrow?"
10. "I won't be late," promised Josie.

## Exercise 7

1. Sara watched television; she had finished her homework.
2. The baby was crying; he was hungry.
3. The old man shivered violently; it was bitterly cold.
4. Mum told him to brush his hair; it was a total mess.
5. She read the book; it was an adventure story.
6. The children went home tired and hungry; they had had enough.
7. I shall take some of the library books back now; the others will have to wait.
8. She had worked very hard for the exam; she hoped it would be enough.
9. It was a warm, sunny day; they decided to go to the seaside.
10. The parcel had been badly wrapped; some of the contents were showing.

## Exercise 8

1. After the match the stadium was covered with rubbish: cigarette packets, beer cans, programmes, newspapers, take-away food wrapping and tickets.
2. There are four varieties of tree in the wood: oak, ash, horsechestnut and sycamore.
3. As I left the house mum said just three words: "Do your best".
4. There are three things about her dog I cannot bear: it smells, it sheds hair, it barks.
5. The results of my examinations were disastrous: I failed.
6. You need to bring some things with you: a pencil, a ruler, paper and a ring-binder.
7. I remember Martin Luther King's words: "I have a dream".
8. There were many things in the cupboard: a pair of gloves, a scarf and a handbag.
9. Three painters represent the Impressionist school of painting: Monet, Renoir and Cezanne.
10. A truss is a measure of weight for two things: hay and straw.

## Exercise 9

1. You should have white wine (served cold) with fish: red wine (served at room temperature) with red meat.
2. My sister, Sophie, is studying anthropology (the science of man) at London University.
3. The English teacher asked us to find the collective term for eggs (clutch), scones (batch) and beautiful ladies (bevy). I was the only one who knew the answers.
4. The unit of currency (money) for Scandinavia is the krone.
5. The Eiffel Tower (984 feet high) is in Paris.
6. The distance travelled by light in one year (about six million million miles) is known as a 'light year'.
7. Our veterinary surgeon F.R.C.V.S. (Fellow of the Royal College of Veterinary Surgeons) is also our next door neighbour.
8. There is an anemometer (wind-guage) in our school garden.
9. St. Paul's Cathedral (built by Sir Christopher Wren) is a well-known feature of the London skyline.
10. The largest anchor carried by a ship (the sheet anchor) is used only in an emergency.

## Exercise 10

1. As soon as the light began to fade – that was early because of the low cloud – they set off back to base camp.
2. As soon as he got a place at university – he worked very hard for that – he went to look for a flat.
3. Auntie Babs – isn't she marvellous for sixty-five? – sent me some money for my birthday.
4. "Well, you see – I mean – oh, please come in!"
5. "Walk, if you please – don't run."
6. Mick Jones, the soccer coach, said that there was only one reason why he had picked Smith for the first eleven – to score goals.
7. They all knew why Sissy won first prize – she was the best.
8. Good advice to people about to hang-glide – don't.
9. She revved-up the car – was she late? – and screeched out of the drive.
10. Christine told her mother what she wanted for Christmas – a computer.

## Exercise 11

1. The bird-bath in the garden is moss-covered.
2. At school Sally is in a class of thirty ten-year-olds.
3. The pink-coloured azalea in the pretty bowl was presented as first prize at the gymkhana.
4. The well-aimed arrow hit the target with precision and scored full marks.
5. "I hope you will co-operate with me," said Miss Jones.
6. John is a self-motivated, well-mannered and self-confident third-form student who should do well.

7.  The tickets were pre-booked.

8.  Non-payment will result in further action.

9.  The lesson lasted for one-and-a-half hours.

10. The music played at three-quarter time.

## Exercise 12

1.  Shaun agreed that the film version of 'Jurassic Park' was better than the book.

2.  For many years the chair person of 'Question Time' was Sir Robin Day.

3.  "Open, Sesme!" were the magic words used in 'Ali Baba and the Forty Thieves'.

4.  Sara went to Stratford-Upon-Avon to see 'Midsummer Night's Dream', her favourite play.

5.  David has just finished reading 'Robinson Crusoe' by Daniel Defoe.

6.  'Neighbours', 'Home and Away' and 'Grangehill' are Michael's favourite television programmes.

7.  Sara so enjoyed reading 'Redwall', 'Mossflower' and 'Salamandastron', that now she is in the bookshop looking for 'Mattimeo' by the same author, Brian Jacques.

8.  'You've Been Framed', 'Blind Date' and 'Crystal Maze' are James' favourite T.V. programmes.

9.  'Witches', 'The Magic Finger' and 'Matilda' are just three of the novels of Roald Dahl.

10. As part of our studies of First World War poets, we are looking at Rupert Brooke's, 'The Soldier'.

## Exercise 13

*Who will free me from this turbulent priest?*

1.  When Henry II described Beckett as "this turbulent priest" of whom he wished to be "free", he did not realise that his faithful followers would indeed carry out his wishes and murder Beckett.

*England is a nation of shopkeepers.*

2.  Napoleon disparagingly describes England as "a nation of shopkeepers".

*Eureka!*

3.  Archimedes, as he stepped into his bath, noticed the displaced water overflowing, and is said to have exclaimed, "Eureka!" Archimedes Principle was discovered.

*Veni, vidi, vici.*

4.  I came, I saw, I conquered: "Veni, vidi, vici," is the famous quotation of Julius Caesar on conquering Britain.

*I like work; it fascinates me. I can sit and look at it for hours.*

5.  "I like work; it fascinates me. I can sit and look at it for hours", is a quotation by Jerome K. Jerome.

## Exercise 14

1.  The children's toys

2.  Mr Williams' boat

3.  The ladies' hats

4.  James' toy train set

5.  Sara's mountain bike

6.  The team's score

7.  The boat's crew

8.  The book's cover

9.  The son-in-law's mother

10. The newsagent's shop.

## Exercise 15

1.  Mrs Jones and Mrs Williams' hats

2.  The students' bags

3.  The trees' leaves

4.  The tree's leaves

5.  Jade and Liam's father

6.  The cat's whiskers

7.  James' sister

8.  The passers-by's glances

9.  The pavement's edge

10. The hairdresser's scissors

## Exercise 16

1.  If you're ready to go, we'll leave.
    I thought we'd go swimming.

2.  It's a lovely day. I thought we'd go for a walk.
    You can come, can't you?

3.  The cat is licking its paw. I think it's hurt it.
    We'll have to take it to the vet.

4.  Won't you turn down that radio?
    I've had about as much as I can take.

5.  Don't do that! We've waited a long time for his call and if you lift the receiver he won't get through.

6.  She hasn't got your tea ready because she wasn't expecting you until later.

7.  It isn't fair. You went first last time. It's my turn.

8.  Couldn't we wait just a little longer? He's probably rushing to us now.

9.  How's your father? I hear he's been unwell.
    I hope he's better soon.

10. There's always a second chance, so don't give up all the hard work. It's worth it in the end.